G000144004

Puss in Boot

by Nick Cornall
edited by Alison Hedger

The traditional pantomime story of Puss in Boots
with six new songs plus optional encore

Duration approx. 50 minutes

For Primary School children with mixed abilities

The main character parts suit KEY STAGE 2
Younger children can join the choir and dancers,
dressed as woodland animals or country folk

TEACHER'S BOOK

Piano score complete with vocal line and chord symbols
Production notes included
Add percussion and sound effects as desired

SONGS

1. Magic, Magic, Everywhere	*All*
2. Everybody Needs Some Money	*All + Mother (optional)*
3. Deep Down In The Woods	*All + Forest Creatures' Dance*
4. Not The Bed Of Roses	*Princess, + All + Princess' Dance*
5. Silly Little Me	*Dobbin + All*
6. Here He Comes	*All*
Finale repeat 1. Magic, Magic, Everywhere	*All*
7. Huff-Huff! Optional Encore	*All + audience*

Incidental music is included

The Pupil's Book contains the play and song words
Order No. GA 11020

A matching tape cassette of the music for rehearsals and performances is available,
Order No. GA11021, side A with vocals included and side B with vocals omitted.

© Copyright 1996 Golden Apple Productions
A division of Chester Music Limited
8/9 Frith Street, London W1V 5TZ

Order No. GA11019

ISBN 0 7119 5606 5

PRODUCTION NOTES

CHARACTERS

	Narrator(s)		
*	Mother	farmer's wife	(*solo singing is optional*)
	Granny		(*non-speaking*)
	Mostwyn	⎫	(*eldest*)
	Godwin	⎬ three brothers	
	Edwin	⎭	(*youngest*)
*	Dobbin	family pet donkey	
	Puss	tabby cat	
* +	Princess		
	Alice	Princess' servant girl	
	Ogre		
	King		
	Chamberlain		
	Palace Servant		(*one line to speak*)
	Owl	⎫	
	Little Bird	⎬ woodland animals	(*speaking*)
	Little Rabbit		
	Little Deer	⎭	
+	Forest Creatures		(*non-speaking*)
	King's Bodyguards		(*non-speaking*)
	King's Entourage		(*non-speaking*)
	Singing Chorus		(*body of singers dressed as country folk or woodland creatures*)

*   indicates solo singing
+   indicates dance: other characters may dance should this be suitable for your production
                    e.g. Dobbin during Song 5

SIX SCENES

1. At The Family Farmhouse
2. In The Woods
3. At The King's Palace
4. Back At The Farmhouse
5. In The Woods Again
6. At The Ogre's Castle

THREE SETS

1. Humble farmhouse interior
2. Woods
3. King's Palace ⎫ *use same set, but hang*
   Ogre's Castle ⎭ *different portraits on walls*

COSTUMES

As one would expect, but it is best for the animals to have their faces uncovered. All dancers should have bare feet, or dancing shoes for the Princess.

PRINCIPAL PROPS

> Father's Will
> Cardboard shotgun
> A big tree
> Filled sack
> Extra large box of stuffing
> Statement of debt
> Blanket

SOUND EFFECTS AND LIGHTING

A loud sound of splashing water is needed for Scene Five. As all the action takes place during daylight hours, no lighting is required for special effects. However, if theatrical lighting is available it will naturally enhance your production.

STAGE DIRECTIONS

These have been kept to the minimum. Use of country and aristocratic dialects will no doubt add to the humour, so long as the children speak slowly and clearly enough for the audience to catch the words and the metre of the verses. Aim to over act, rather than under act gestures.

MATCHING AUDIO CASSETTE

All Golden Apple titles have a matching tape cassette of the music to help the children learn the songs. The tape for PUSS IN BOOTS will also let you hear how the music goes should you need some help in this. If you are single-handed at rehearsals the tape will leave you free to move about as necessary. Side A has the song words added, but these are left out on the B side, so you can use the tape for performances.

A MESSAGE FROM NICK CORNALL

PUSS IN BOOTS was written with the wide variety of skills and abilities of the Primary school in mind. The principal parts will stretch the more able child, whilst there are plenty of parts for those to whom acting and learning come less easily. The script is in verse which greatly assists learning.

I staged PUSS IN BOOTS in the round with all the children being seated around the stage area. All the children were involved all the time. But the pantomime will also work well on a traditional stage.

Finally, have you considered a parent choir? A real sense of community can be engendered this way. Two rehearsals are more than enough.

1
MAGIC, MAGIC, EVERYWHERE

All
(Opens Scene One)
Finale cue: . . . Very first aristo-cat .

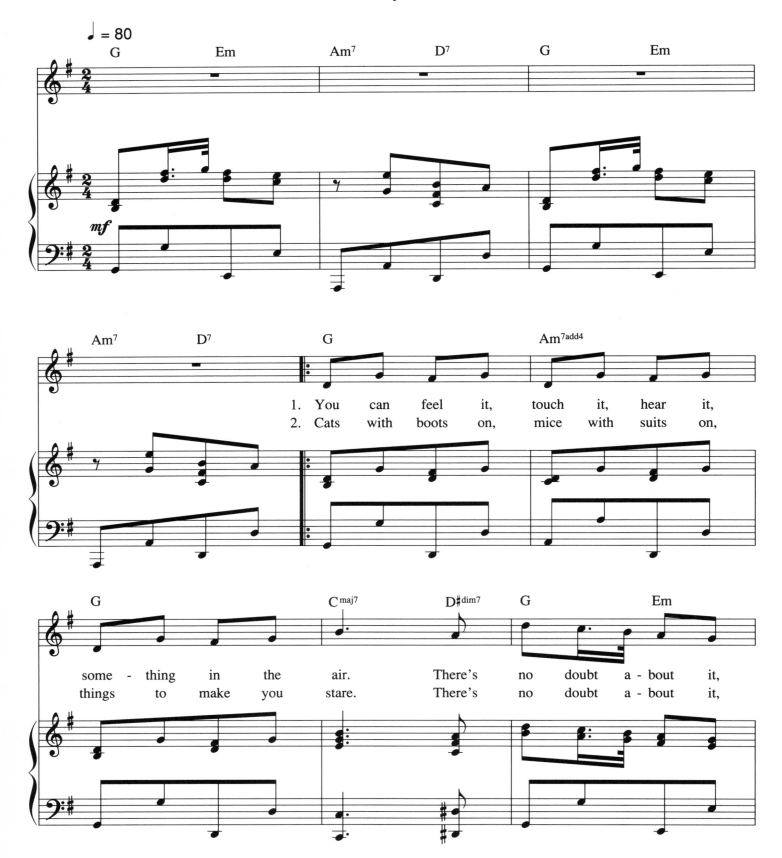

1. You can feel it, touch it, hear it,
2. Cats with boots on, mice with suits on,

some - thing in the air. There's no doubt a - bout it,
things to make you stare. There's no doubt a - bout it,

When you are de - ter - mined there's no such word as

can't! 4. Gob - lins talk - ing, witch - es stalk - ing,

crea - tures strange and rare. There's no doubt a - bout it,

ma - gic's ev - e - ry - where.

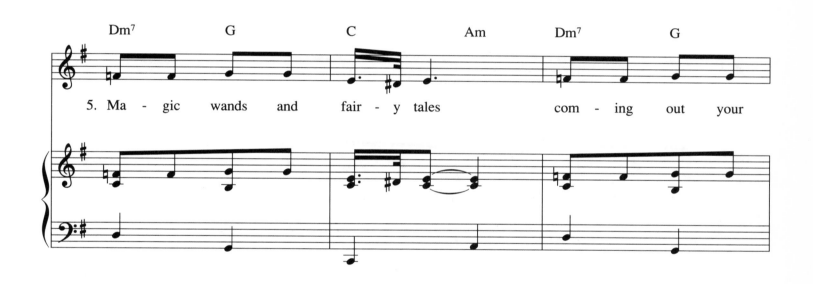

5. Ma - gic wands and fair - y tales com - ing out your

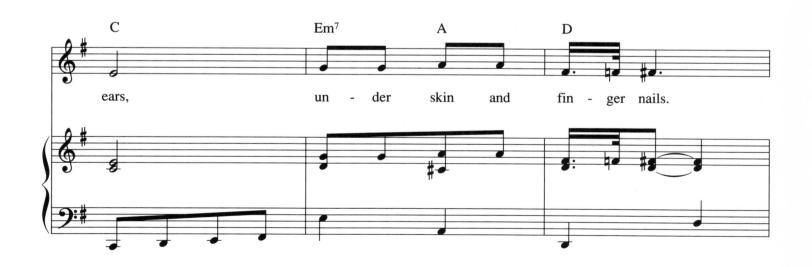

ears, un - der skin and fin - ger nails.

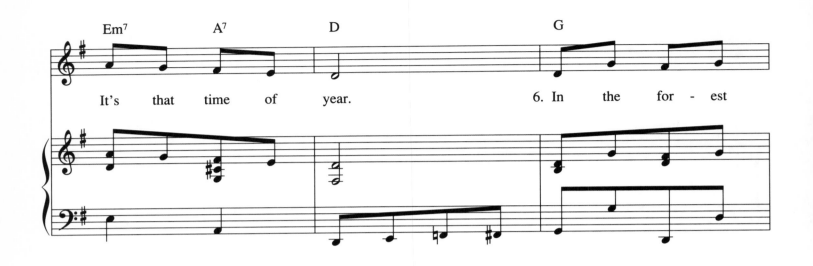

It's that time of year. 6. In the for - est

have you no - ticed some - thing in the air? There's

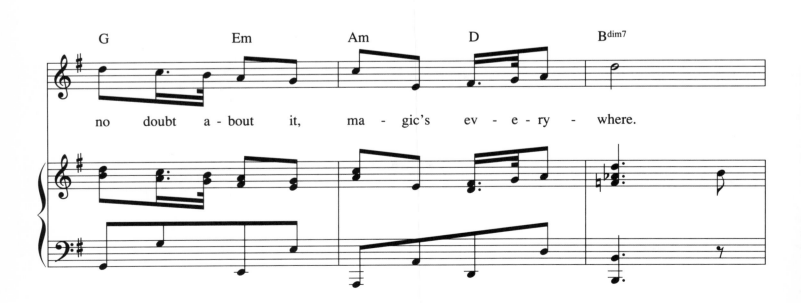

no doubt a - bout it, ma - gic's ev - e - ry - where.

Ma - gic, ma - gic, ev - ery - where.

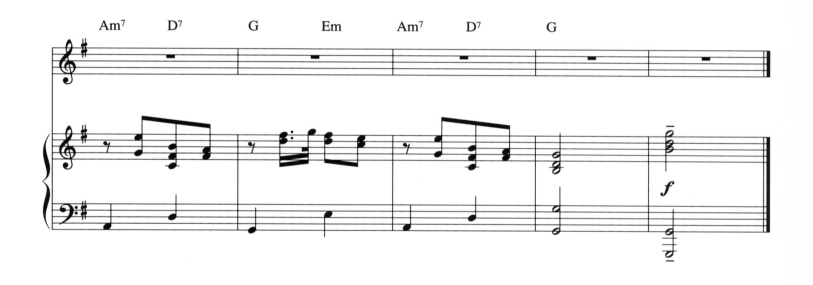

2
EVERYBODY NEEDS SOME MONEY

All + Mother (optional for verse 5)
other verses can also be delegated if desired

Cue: . . . To leave me any thistles.

1. Ev - ery - bod - y needs some mon - ey, ev - ery - bod - y needs some
2. Ev - ery time I think of mon - ey, I can feel my heart go

dosh. If you have - n't got a quid or two, your
boom. All I want to be's a mil - lion - aire, it

heart feels heav - y. You feel blue and . . .
is - n't much. It seems quite fair to me.

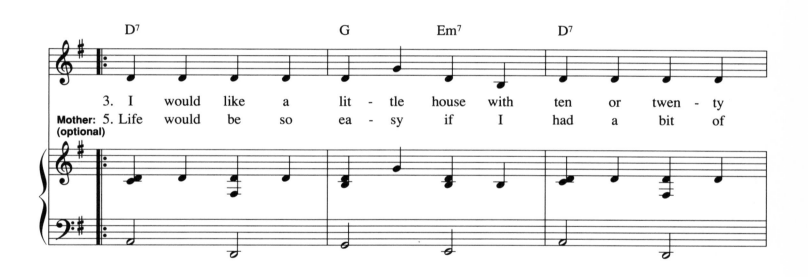

3. I would like a lit - tle house with ten or twen - ty
Mother: 5. Life would be so ea - sy if I had a bit of
(optional)

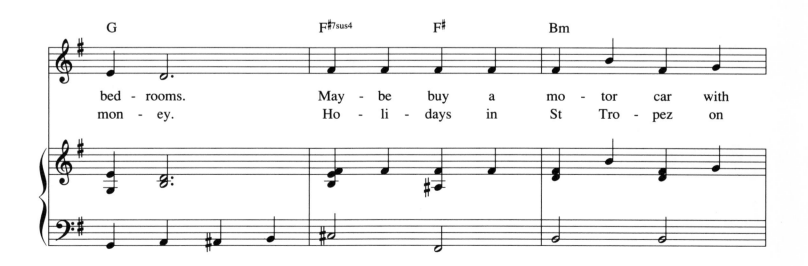

bed - rooms. May - be buy a mo - tor car with
mon - ey. Ho - li - days in St Tro - pez on

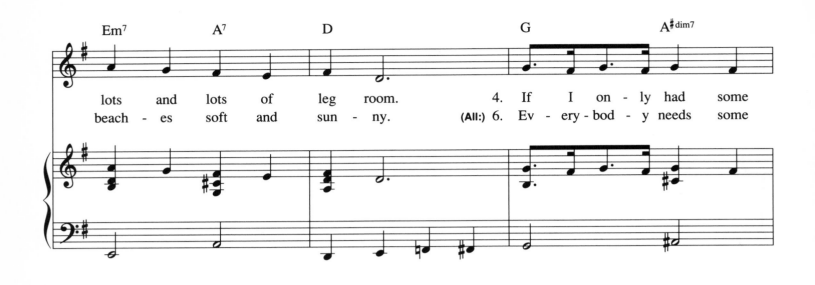

lots   and   lots   of   leg room.   4. If   I   on - ly   had   some
beach - es   soft   and   sun - ny.   **(All:)** 6. Ev - ery - bod - y   needs   some

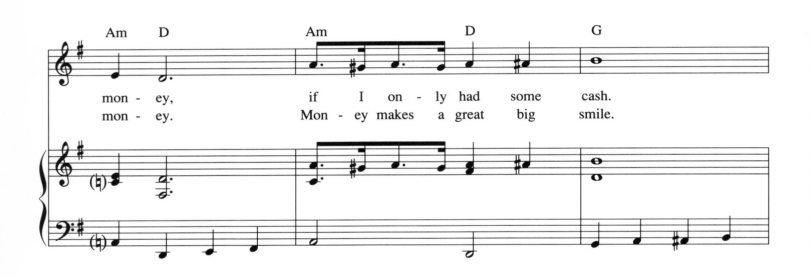

mon - ey,   if   I   on - ly   had   some   cash.
mon - ey.   Mon - ey makes   a   great   big   smile.

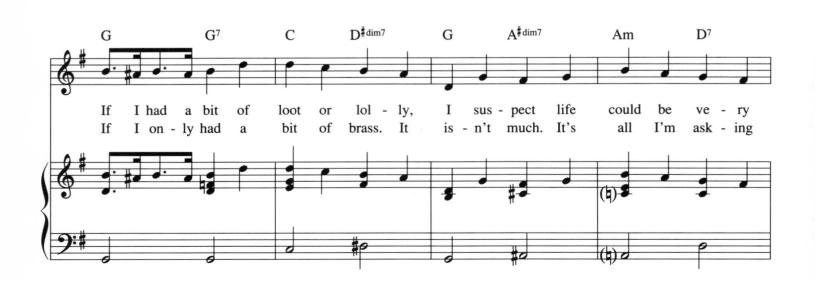

If   I   had   a   bit   of   loot   or   lol - ly,   I   sus - pect   life   could   be   ve - ry
If   I   on - ly   had   a   bit   of   brass.   It   is - n't   much.   It's   all   I'm   ask - ing

good.   for.

Coda

Just   a   lit - tle bit   of   dough,   or   dosh,   or

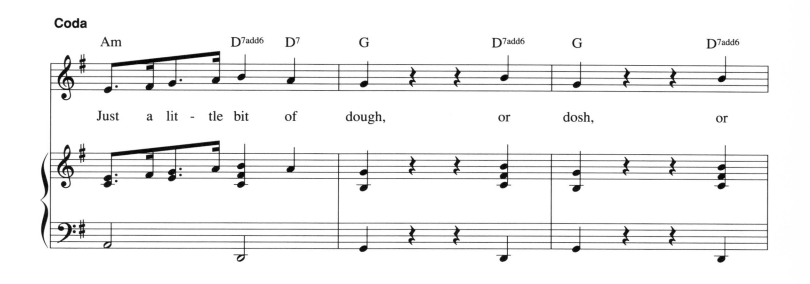

cash,   or   brass,   or   loot.

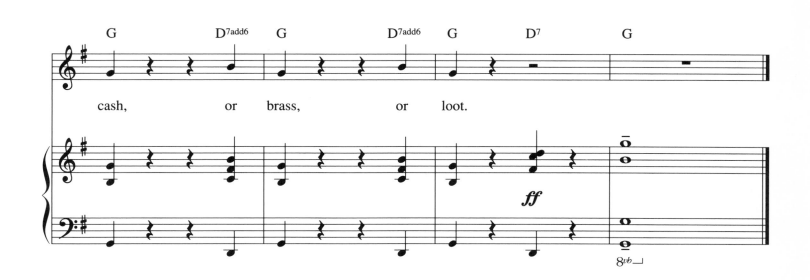

13

MUSIC FOR END OF SCENE ONE

Cue: . . . For some anti-Histamine.

3
DEEP DOWN IN THE WOODS

All + Forest Creatures' Dance
(Opens Scene Two)

1. Deep down in the woods where the
bad - ger's a - bout and the
cloud in the sky, there's no

crea - tures are good, the sun shines near - ly ev - ery day.
sky - lark is out, the squir - rels are an - y - thing but grey.
rea - son to cry, for dan - ger's ve - ry far a - way.

If you lis - ten you can hear the sound of wood - land folk at

Refrain

play. Buzz, buzz go the bees, and the birds in the trees are sing - ing the whole day

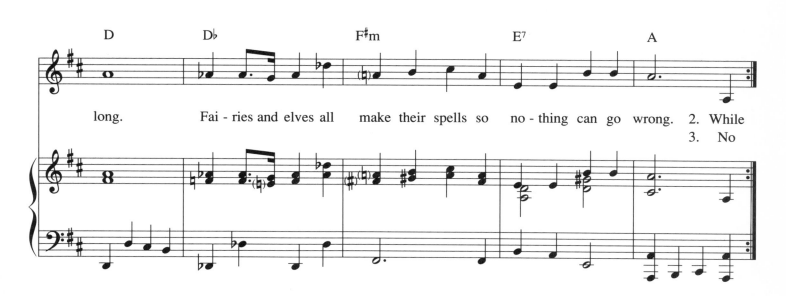

long. Fai - ries and elves all make their spells so no - thing can go wrong. 2. While
3. No

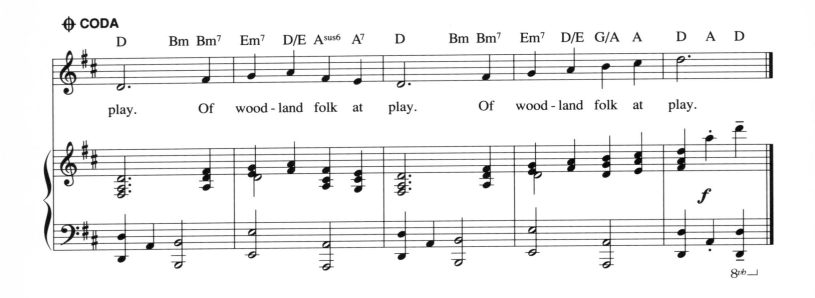

OGRE MUSIC
from Song 6

Cue: . . . I'm really frightened.

Repeat music as many times as needed. Begin slowly and quietly. Music is played as pantomime routine takes place. Gradually get faster as the Ogre chases Dobbin off stage.

MUSIC FOR END OF SCENE TWO

Cue: What's that? Lots of dosh!

FANFARE TO OPEN SCENE THREE

Repeat as necessary

Piano

Try two-part
descant recorders:

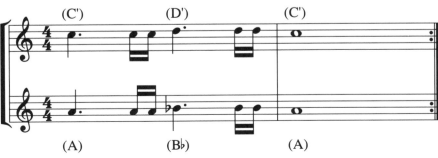

4
NOT THE BED OF ROSES

Princess + All + Princess' Dance

Cue: . . . Chamberlain, let's go and count some money.
(End of Scene Three)

chance to come and join the mon - ar - chy.   2. My en -
all have knock knees and a ghast - ly   squint?   **Princess:** It's

(Refrain)
♩ = 104

not much fun when you're the prize that's sought by ev - ery-

(Princess dances whilst All sing repeat)

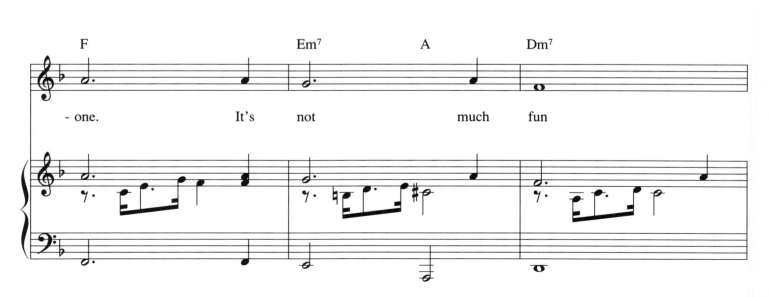

- one.   It's not much fun

when you have ad-mi-rers by the ton! It is-n't ve-ry charm-ing___ and it

is-n't ve-ry nice, when you are the wed-ding cake and ev-ery-

-bod-y wants a slice!_____ So if you think it's ea-sy, I sug-

-gest that you think twice. It's not much fun, it's

not much fun. **All:** It's

MUSIC TO OPEN SCENE FOUR

5

SILLY LITTLE ME

Dobbin + All

Cue: There's nothing left to lose.
(End of Scene Four)

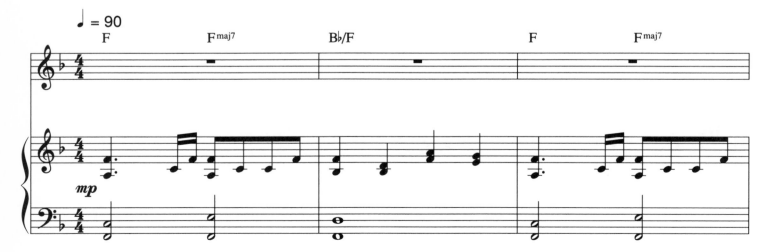

Refrain

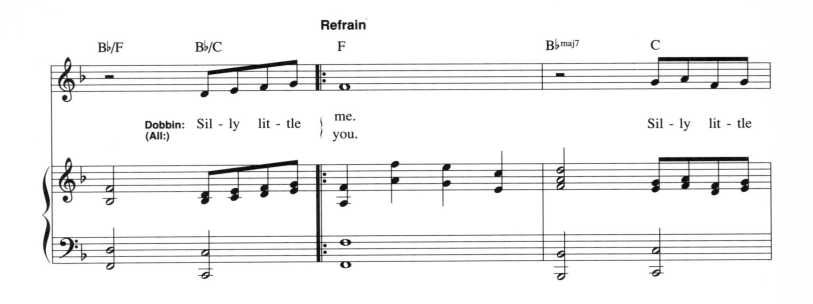

Dobbin: Sil - ly lit - tle { me. / you.

Sil - ly lit - tle

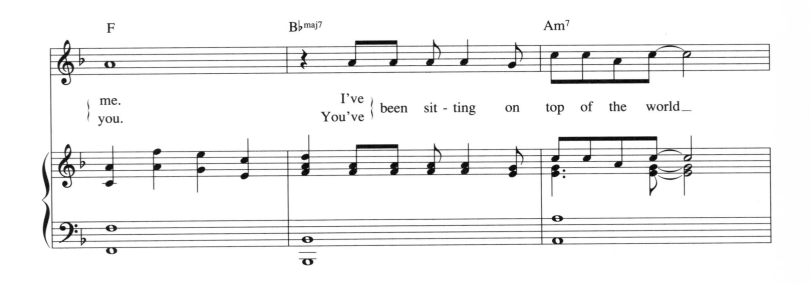

{ me. / you. }
I've / You've been sit - ting on top of the world

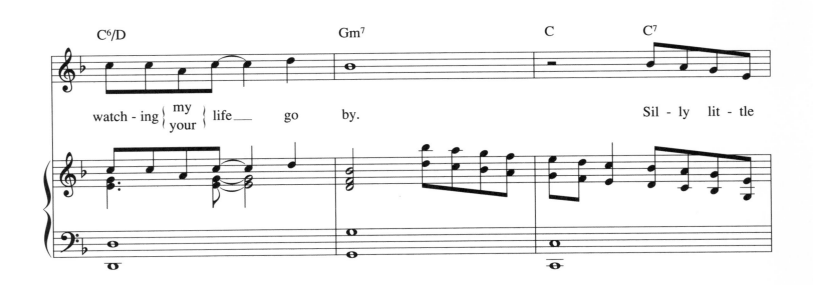

watch - ing { my / your } life go by.

Sil - ly lit - tle

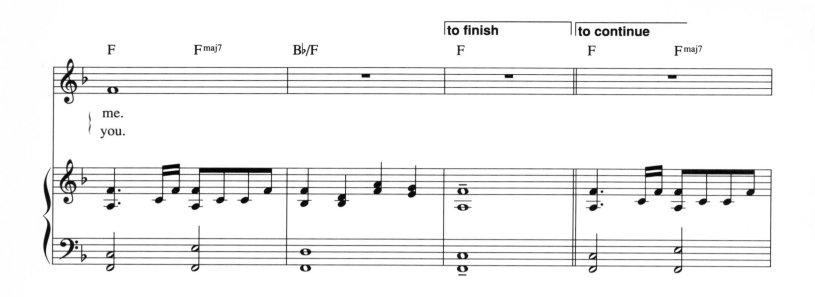

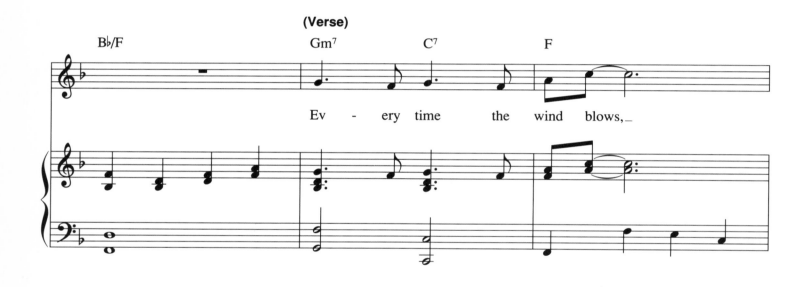

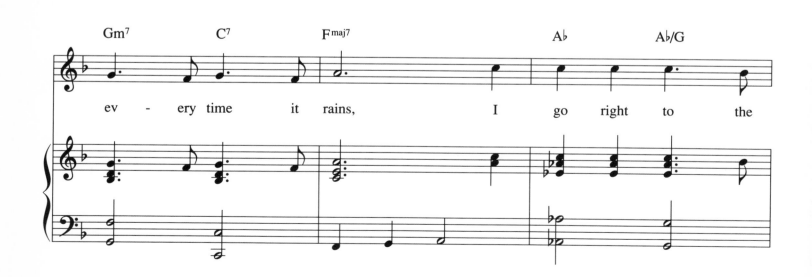

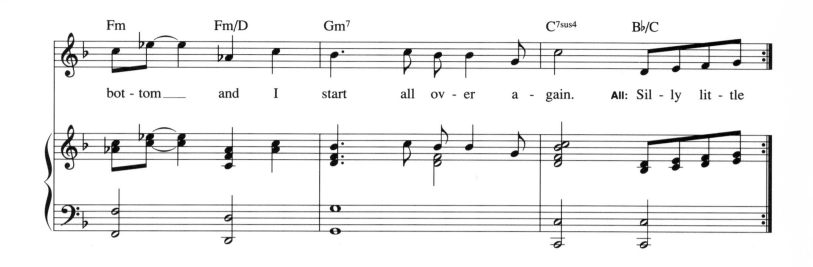

bot - tom_____ and I start all ov - er a - gain. **All:** Sil - ly lit - tle

REPRISE 3
DEEP DOWN IN THE WOODS

All + optional repeat of Forest Creatures' Dance

(Opens Scene Five)

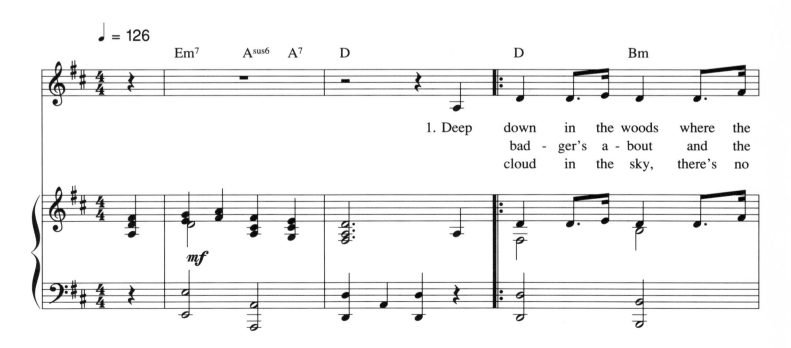

1. Deep down in the woods where the
bad - ger's a - bout and the
cloud in the sky, there's no

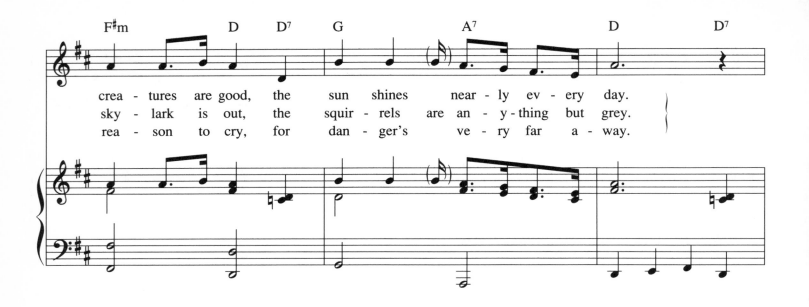

crea - tures are good, the sun shines near - ly ev - ery day.
sky - lark is out, the squir - rels are an - y - thing but grey.
rea - son to cry, for dan - ger's ve - ry far a - way.

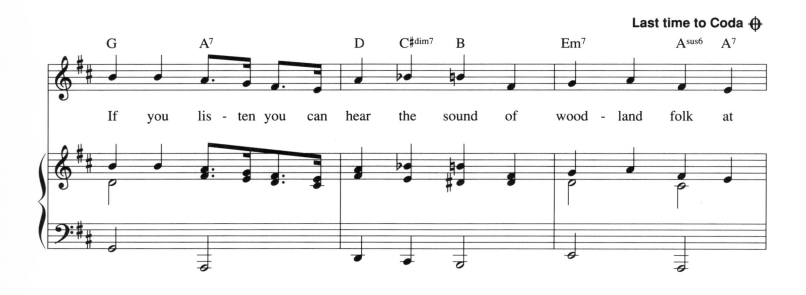

Last time to Coda

If you lis - ten you can hear the sound of wood - land folk at

Refrain

play. Buzz, buzz go the bees, and the birds in the trees are sing - ing the whole day

long.   Fai - ries and elves all   make their spells so   no - thing can go wrong.   2. While
                                                                                                                                   3.   No

CODA

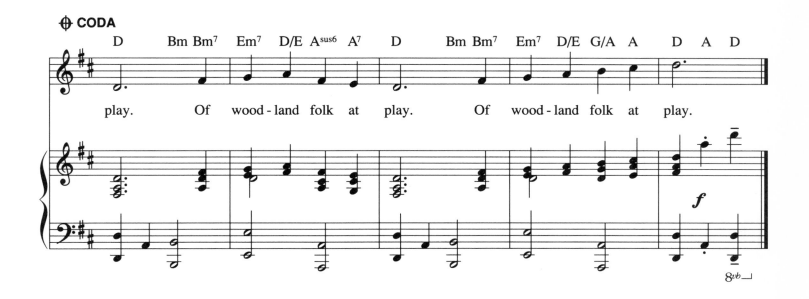

play.   Of   wood - land folk at   play.   Of   wood - land folk at   play.

6
HERE HE COMES

All

Cue: . . . What? Slap your thighs!
(End of Scene Five)

It's the Og - re, rum - pi - ty tum.

1. Deep in the
2. Down in the

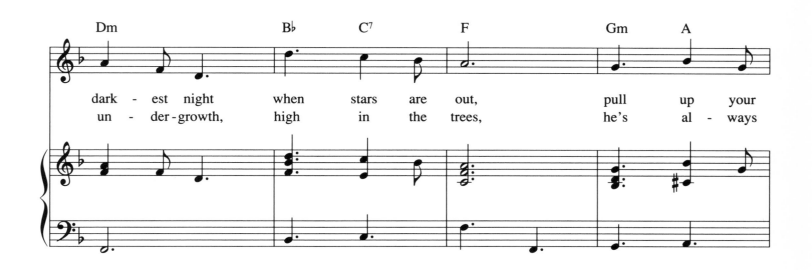

dark - est night when stars are out, pull up your
un - der - growth, when high in the trees, he's al - ways

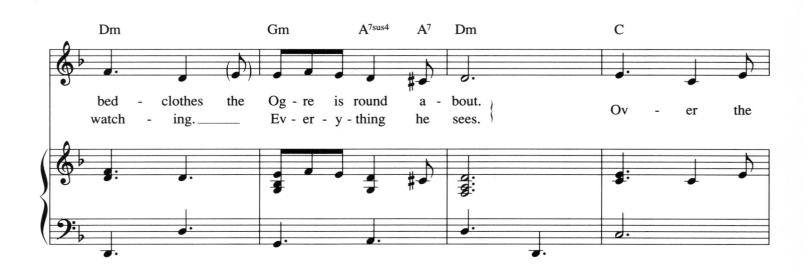

bed - clothes the Og - re is round a - bout.
watch - ing. Ev - er - y - thing he sees.

Ov - er the

roof - tops when frost is deep, he'll come and

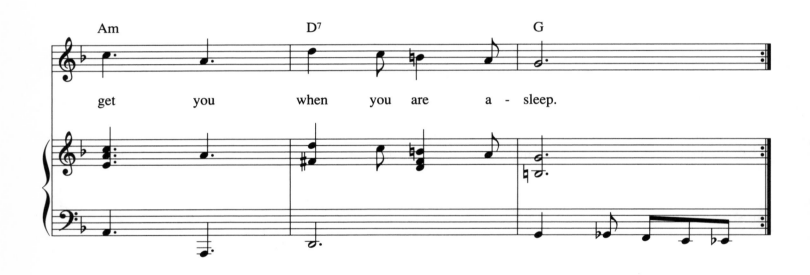

get you when you are a - sleep.

Refrain

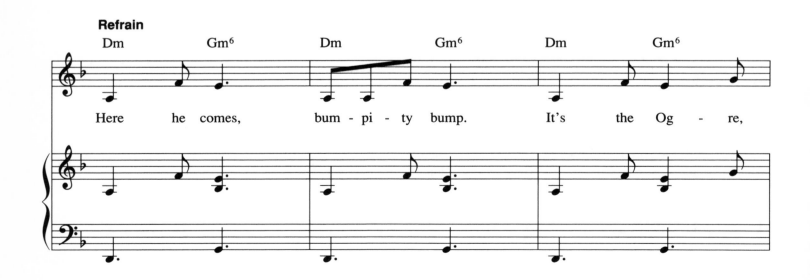

Here he comes, bum - pi - ty bump. It's the Og - re,

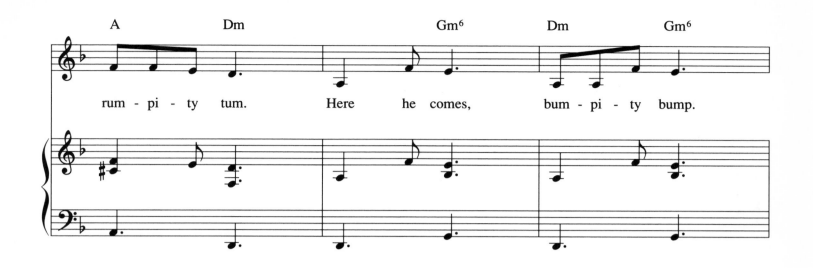

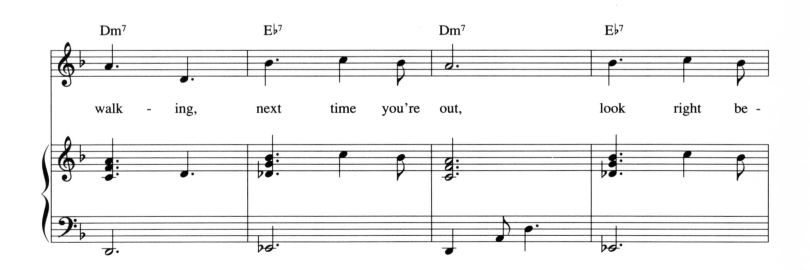

-hind   you,   the   Og – re   is   here   a – bout.

MUSIC TO OPEN SCENE SIX

OGRE MUSIC

Cue: . . . Is thoroughly petrified.

Repeat music as many times as needed. Begin slowly and quietly. Music is played as the action routine takes place. Gradually get faster and louder, finishing with a very loud chord. Dobbin is left on stage to face the Ogre alone.

FINALE
Repeat 1.
MAGIC, MAGIC, EVERYWHERE
All
(turn back to page 4)

EXPLANATORY NOTES FOR THE OPTIONAL ENCORE
7.
HUFF-HUFF!
(page 36)

Two confident children lead the proceedings. Large song words are displayed.

1: As is traditional, we are going to end with a song for everyone.
2: The children will sing it through for you, then it will be your turn to join in.

(sing song)

1: Right, now we'll point to the words, as we want everyone to join in.
2: Anyone who doesn't join in will be in BIG trouble!

(sing song pointing to words)

1: What do you think of that?
2: A bit weedy in the huff-huff department!
1: I know what you mean. I don't think everyone was really trying their best! This time let's watch out for those not pulling their weight!

(sing song pointing to words)

1: Well, that was a LITTLE better, but I think we could do with an adult leading the huffs from the front.
2: Let's ask a teacher to choose a grown-up to come up here with us.

(victim(s) is suitably coerced onto the stage)

1: Now, we can rely on you to lead some ENORMOUS huffs can't we?
2: Here we go!

(sing song letting "victim(s)" take solo refrain. Applaud their efforts)

1: Now, once more . . . all together . . .

(sing song, this time with the Refrain at double speed)

OPTIONAL ENCORE

7.

HUFF-HUFF!

All + Audience

At places marked * blow as rudely as circumstances allow!

Now the play is near - ly through.

That's be - yond a doubt. Just one thing re -

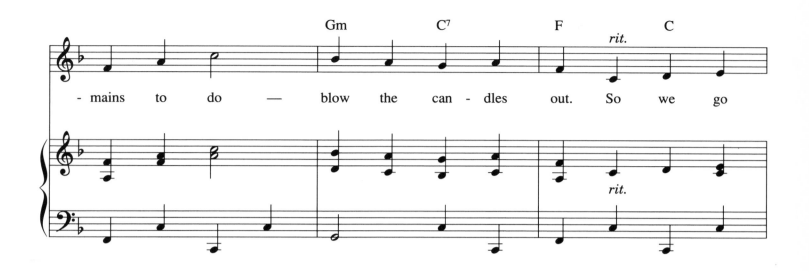

-mains to do — blow the can- dles out. So we go

Refrain
a tempo

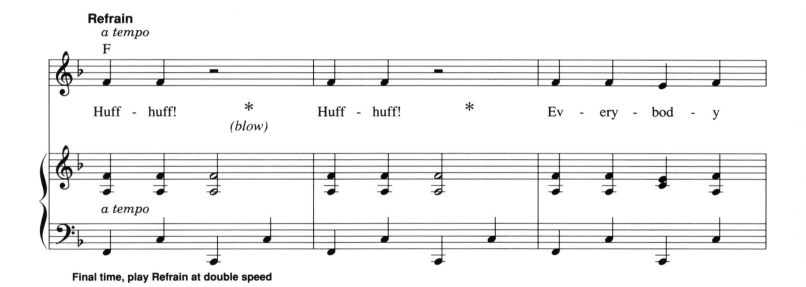

Huff - huff!   *   Huff - huff!   *   Ev - ery - bod - y
(blow)

Final time, play Refrain at double speed

blow!   Huff - huff!   *   Huff - huff!   *

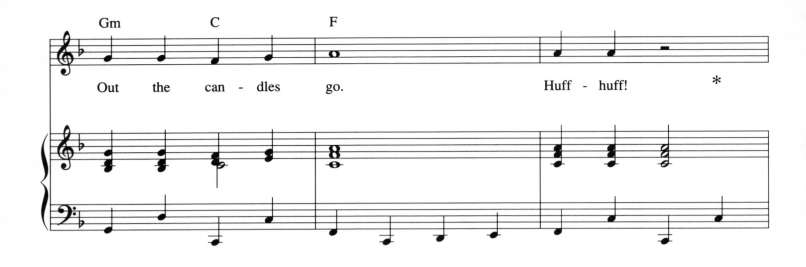

Printed in England by Caligraving Limited Thetford Norfolk

Puss in Boots by Jo aged 12 years